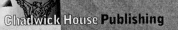

A Guide to Customer Perceptions of Food Hygiene

Dr Jeremy Leach

Chadwick House Publishing

Chadwick Court

15 Hatfields, London

SE1 8DJ, England

Publications

Tel: 0207 827 5830

Fax: 0207 827 9930

Email: Publications@chgl.com

Web: www.chgl.com

ISBN: 1-904306-00-4

To Rachel for her love and support

The Chadwick House Publishing series on Food

Contents

The Author

Jeremy C Leach, BA, PhD, MCIEH, FRSH, FRIPH is an experienced Environmental Health Practitioner currently working in Sussex. He qualified in 1978 from the University of the West of England (formerly Bristol Polytechnic). Since that date he has undertaken most of the environmental health specialisms, including many years enforcing food safety legislation. Latterly he has been working with businesses through training and other proactive initiatives to improve standards of food hygiene.

Jeremy Leach has always been interested in people and the way that everyone interacts and behaves. Because of this interest he decided to study for a degree in psychology-based subjects with the Open University. In 1999 he was awarded the degree of Doctor of Philosophy by the University of Brighton in collaboration with King's College, London for a thesis about public and professional perceptions of food hygiene in public-eating places.

He has written articles and pieces for numerous professional journals and trade magazines and is in demand as a conference and seminar presenter. He passionately believes that customers should be taking a larger part in improving food hygiene and general cleanliness standards by not supporting those few businesses which continually offer low standards and who do the catering industry no favours

The author may be contacted via the publishers.

Chapter 1
About this book

This book draws upon research which involved members of the public and professionals working in the catering field or connected with it, the later including caterers, trainers and environmental health practitioners. The research focused on the perceptions of food hygiene in public eating-places. In addition the author has also contributed his own expertise, founded on over twenty years of working as an environmental health practitioner, both from an enforcement perspective and as a trainer working with proprietors of businesses and employees to improve standards of food hygiene.

The contents of this book aim to help proprietors, managers and staff of restaurants, hotels, cafés, public houses, take-aways – in fact all types of business involved in catering – to deliver excellent service in the areas of food hygiene and cleanliness from a customers perspective. In addition, although the messages in this book are aimed primarily at the catering sector, they are also just as relevant and important to the food retail sector.

The chapters that follow are divided into definitive areas of a typical business. This, it is hoped, will make the book highly readable, logical and useful as a reference, and also a possible training aid. At the end of the book are a series of appendices; these are designed to accompany the chapters. Each appendix includes a checklist and comment sheet, allowing you to use them for internal audits so that the performance of your business in each of the areas can be assessed. Where improvements are needed then these can be noted and appropriate action taken. The items in the checklists are the clues which members of the public and those in the industry or connected with it say that they may look for when assessing the standards of food hygiene and cleanliness of any food-related business. Remember that one of these people could be your next customer.

Also included are direct quotes from the research, these are used to highlight a particular point. Using the words stated at the time of an interview or written on a questionnaire form can bring the text to life and relay experiences and thoughts in a very real way. Where quotes have been used in this way, you will find that immediately underneath the quote will be the source. If it is a member of the public then the gender and age range of that person will be shown. Similarly quotes from a professional will be attributed to the individual professions.

This book is not a guide to the law or in any way gives guidance on compliance with the various Acts of Parliament and associated Regulations. There are plenty of texts available which will give you that information. Advice on legal compliance is also available from the environmental health department of your local authority.

The concept of a written food hazard analysis system is becoming more common and no doubt will become a legal requirement in due course. Such systems require most attention to be placed on those points in any catering or food retail operation which are critical to food safety, thereby improving the safety of the food and protecting public health. After all that is what all hazard analysis systems are about – taking a logical and systematic look at your operation so that nothing gets missed, then deciding along the way where significant hazards exist and developing simple controls and checks at those points where the safety of the food and ultimately your customers' health may be in jeopardy. Any hazard analysis system should also be underpinned by good hygiene practices and policies relating to such issues as personal hygiene, cleaning and disinfection and pest control.

The drawback with this approach for the business person is that the little details, which may not represent a risk to the health of customers but which can deleteriously affect the reputation and attractiveness of the business to potential and repeat custom, can get overlooked. This is where this book will be a tremendous help. The demands of hazard analysis can place the proprietor of a food business in a dilemma: where do they focus their scarce resources, on a system designed to provide safe food to the customers and thereby protecting them or on measures to attract them? Of course in reality the answer must be both, as both will prevent disaster and deliver success for that business in the long run.

Following years of experience of inspecting food businesses for compliance with hygiene laws and by watching the many television programmes that have particularly concentrated on food hygiene, it has always amazed me the poor hygiene conditions under which a minority of businesses operate. When you see some of the places I have seen or watched with amazement some of those stomach-churning television programmes, it surprises me that any customers ever patronise those businesses at all – I certainly would not! In addition a few proprietors, in my experience, also seem to wait for the local authority officer to audit their business for food hygiene purposes for them. Those few proprietors then know that they will get a schedule of works from the local authority of essential items upon which to act. While this is very flattering, everyone should know that the law mainly demands a relatively low standard and it is not exactly a proactive stance to take on the management of such an essential aspect of any food business.

However, proprietors of businesses should also be aware that increasingly inspections undertaken by officers from local authority environmental health departments are focusing on the factors which are a risk to food safety and therefore public health. Some of those factors, which this research highlighted and which are detailed in the following chapters, may get missed.

There is also an enforcement culture, encouraged by successive governments, which takes on a 'laissez faire' approach and very much a partnership and working with business to improve standards, rather than a strict enforcement regime. While this is very laudable and positive it is an approach exploited by some to continue maintaining poor or mediocre standards. Unfortunately it is these businesses which are always featured in the news and in documentary programmes and it is these which give the whole food industry a bad name.

There is a tendency over time, when we work, day in, day out, somewhere, for us all to become blind to the standards under which we operate. It is to be hoped that this book will open your eyes to those sometimes forgotten details, which can do so much to maintain customer confidence.

Chapter 2
Setting the scene

Introduction

There is no doubt that customers are becoming more discerning and willing to vote with their feet if they are not happy with the standards of food hygiene and general cleanliness offered to them. With an increasing amount of choice available to consumers and aggressive marketing campaigns by some, proprietors and managers of food businesses need to be more aware than ever before of the complex pattern of consumer demands, including that of supplying a clean and safe product in clean and safe conditions.

This situation will only become of heightened importance to business as the Food Standards Agency promulgates information and raises the profile of the subject.

One of the key priorities for the Food Standards Agency is the aim to reduce food-borne illness by 20 per cent improving food safety right through the food chain (Food Standards Agency, 2001b). As this aim is converted into action it is bound to increase awareness and knowledge of food safety issues among the public – indeed it would fail as an aim if it did not achieve this. It is likely therefore that the campaign as it progresses will use a variety of media to put the message across, including radio, television, magazines, newspapers and leaflets.

It is considered unfortunate that such campaigns often use a caricature of a chef or a dirty restaurant to make their points. This is unfair on an industry which relies, to a certain extent, on image and trust by customers that all steps will be taken to protect customers' health. Such images created thrive on stereotypes of the 'dirty café' and then go on to reinforce those images in many people's minds. It is also unfair to portray chefs with dirty overalls and poor habits to make a point. While there are some chefs like this, for those who have been trained in their craft and work hard to maintain high standards the images are to say the least, insulting.

Activity in relation to food safety may also be increased in our schools, arming school students with a greater knowledge and awareness. One of the outcomes of a national campaign such as this will be a more demanding customer who will be looking for high standards of food hygiene and cleanliness. As Engel et al. (1986) wrote:

It all comes down to this essential point, understanding consumer motivation and behaviour is not an option – it is an absolute necessity for competitive survival.

The power of the customer is a theme of a number of writers on the subject of management and marketing and many come to the same conclusion: that those businesses which can give their customers what they want will continue to succeed and those that do not are likely to fail. It is the customer therefore who is the only person who can deliver profits to a company and income for its owners and employees. As Drucker (1989) wrote:

> It is the customer who determines what a business is. For it is the customer and he alone who through being willing to pay for a good or for a service converts economic resources into wealth ...

On a similar theme the Government's Consumer White Paper, Modern Markets: Confident Consumers (Department of Trade and Industry, 1999), makes it clear that confident, knowledgeable and demanding customers are viewed as good for business. The government claims that the most successful businesses are those that anticipate consumer needs, but all will face competitive pressures if they fail to respond. In addition the White Paper asserts that good information helps consumers make the best choices and the better informed they are, the readier they will be to complain and the more business will be under pressure to improve performance and customer services.

> **'Customers take high standards of food hygiene and cleanliness for granted, as part and parcel of eating out.'**

Research undertaken by the author (Leach, 1999), suggests that customers take high standards of food hygiene and cleanliness for granted, as part and parcel of eating out. Paradoxically the same customers also claim to look for many different clues relating to the standards of food hygiene. This contradiction may be explained by the view that it is only when customers spot things that are wrong do they start looking for other clues to support that view. The following statement made by a respondent to the research summarises this explanation:

... I form impressions, I glance at things as I look around; if they're good impressions then I feel comfortable and relaxed. But if they're not so favourable impressions then I feel more on edge and I look for other things that may be wrong. I think that we are reviewing our surroundings all the time. (Female: 55 – 64)

Public and business attitudes to food safety

As customers do take food hygiene standards and general cleanliness for granted, it begs the question why many senior operational managers and supervisors in the catering sector deem food hygiene as significant only when something goes wrong. According to the researchers who came to this conclusion (Guerrier et al, 1992) the subjects were not considered as making a positive contribution towards quality and were unlikely to be viewed in the same terms as other quality variables. The results do raise the question whether managers in the catering sector might still underestimate the significance that the public attaches to food safety.

Goode et al. (1995) revealed, following research, that far more people mistrust companies and the government to provide safe food than trust them. Farmers only fare slightly better. It would be interesting to repeat that research now, following the formation of the Food Standards Agency, which was set up partly to boost consumer confidence in the government to ensure that our food is safe.

The second annual report on consumer attitudes to food standards (Food Standards Agency, 2002a) revealed that more than half of all the consumers surveyed expressed concern about standards of hygiene in one or more food or catering outlets. While the majority of types of food outlets were mentioned in the report, it would appear that most work to improve consumers concerns needs to be addressed by mobile food outlets, take-aways and fast food outlets.

The lack of importance sometimes attached to food safety by proprietors, managers, supervisors and staff is found to be commonly demonstrated during training sessions and courses in food hygiene. In the author's experience candidates are commonly encouraged to list the benefits to a business of having high standards of food hygiene. The list contents can normally be grouped under three headings:

- legal – such as compliance with the law, ie less chance of being prosecuted;
- preventative – such as less chance of food poisoning, less food wastage, less attractive to pests;
- customer orientated benefits – such as reputation, higher sales and so on.

Once those benefits have been identified however, the focus for many candidates returns to the minimum required by the law. Yet in many cases, as is highlighted in this book, customers demand a higher level of food hygiene and cleanliness than the law requires. It would appear that although proprietors, managers, supervisors and staff in the food retail and catering sectors are aware that high standards of food hygiene and cleanliness are important, the criteria are more commonly viewed by them in a much more of a negative and legalistic way. Yet supporting and maintaining high standards of food hygiene and cleanliness can be just, if not more, important to the customer than the furniture, decor and general ambience in a place. A serious food poisoning outbreak will devastate a business and the effects will be widespread and long lasting, much more so than a lapse in other quality variables.

> 'In many cases customers demand a higher level of food hygiene and cleanliness than the law requires.'

An issue of quality

Ask any person in the food retail or catering sector if they would like to improve their business's reputation, please customers and put a smile on the face of the local authority environmental health officer into the bargain and the answer for most would be a resounding 'yes'.

On visiting any food shop or catering establishment, customers experience a whole package of quality variables, including the food, the service, the furnishings, the tableware, the standards of food hygiene and the general cleanliness. These aspects of the service provided can be embraced under the term 'service quality'.

There is an argument – which must be recognised – suggesting that standards of food hygiene for eating places are laid down in law, are not variable and should not therefore be in the quality variable equation. The law, however, is open to interpretation, contains many exemptions and is of a relatively low standard, much lower interestingly than the public expect. According to Wheelock (1992) the United Kingdom food industry needs to place greater emphasis on genuine quality and, by doing so, public confidence in the industry would be increased.

The consumer, according to McMahon and Schmelzer (1989), leads the quality of any service encounter. As East (1993) puts it:

> Quality is not about being the best or the most expensive restaurant or hotel but simply about meeting customers' needs.

East (1993) went on to note that by tradition, quality has generally been associated with products because somehow they seem easier to draw up specifications for, and to measure, monitor and reject them if they do not meet the criteria. However, quality in the service industries is just as important and standards should be set, monitored and appropriate action taken if the service does not meet the standards. The checklists in the appendices to this book will help with this proactive approach.

Many interesting lessons on the subjects of quality and service can be learned from research undertaken by Zeithaml et al (1990). Their research showed that the essential characteristic to ensuring good service quality is meeting or preferably exceeding what customers expect from the service. The researchers went on to define service quality as perceived by customers as:

> the extent of discrepancy between customers' expectations or desires and their perceptions.

From their study, Zeithaml et al (1990) found common themes emerging from the focus group discussions which suggested several essential factors which might shape customers' expectations. These included word-of-mouth communications, personal needs, past experience and external communications.

Johns and Howard (1998) supported this definition, claiming that service quality has no true existence outside the customer's perception. The key therefore to the delivery of a high quality service is to balance customers' expectations and their perceptions and close the gap between the two. Based upon these principles, if a food shop or catering outlet fails to meet the standards of food hygiene and cleanliness expected by customers (this will include both tangible and service issues), then those customers will assess the business as offering a poor quality service. Conversely, if the reality is equal or greater than the expectations, then the customer will assess the service offered as high quality.

As will be seen from the checklists in the Appendix, customers will be coming to food shops and catering establishments with already high expectations. There is evidence to suggest that customers take food hygiene standards for granted, as part and parcel of eating out, as this respondent stated:

> I tend to think food hygiene in an eating-place is automatic, I tend to take it for granted. (Male: 25 – 34)

The results of the research project created 144 clues from the public, which they claim to consider when assessing the standards of food hygiene in any eating-place. The research required the respondents to judge each clue in terms of its degree of importance. While not all of these clues are featured in this book, the important ones are. The public also claim that while they take standards of food hygiene and general cleanliness for granted, if they see things which are wrong, this puts doubts in their minds. The following statement summarises this view:

> If I notice something which is below par, then I will look for other things and I suppose it turns into a checklist. (Male: 55 – 64)

Further evidence suggests that for some, menu cost too, can have a bearing on the standards of food hygiene and general cleanliness in any establishment, but for the others – and indeed for all the professional group – standards of food hygiene and general cleanliness should be high irrespective of the price paid for the meal.

> Hygiene standards should be the same whether you are spending £1.50 or £100 on a meal. (Catering professional)

Putting customers at their ease

Seeing or experiencing something which is not expected creates a feeling of mental unease. This phenomenon is termed cognitive dissonance and is defined as:

> An emotional state setup when two simultaneously held attitudes or cognition's are inconsistent or when there is conflict between belief and overt behaviour. (Reber, 1985)

Let us relate that definition to food hygiene and general cleanliness in any catering or food retail environment. If a person believed as a general rule, and not unreasonably, that eating places or food retail environments should basically be clean and hygienic, but the experience in a particular business is contrary to that belief, then this may lead to cognitive dissonance. That person will feel uneasy about their choice.

Alternatively, or in addition, the belief or mental picture about a premises may also be created by sales or advertising literature and if the experience is not matched to the mental picture then cognitive dissonance may also be experienced.

The theory of cognitive dissonance was first put forward by Leon Festinger (1957). This theory proposed that the existence of dissonance, being psychologically uncomfortable, would motivate a person to take steps to reduce the dissonance and achieve consonance or mental harmony, as that is a much more comfortable state for human beings. In addition, according to the theory, the person will actively avoid situations which are likely to increase dissonance.

Therefore, placing this in context, if after selecting an eating-place a customer starts to be concerned about the hygiene of the premises or the safety of the food, they will start to experience doubts about the wisdom of their choice of eating-place; according to Festinger (1957) they will be experiencing 'post decisional dissonance'. This may or may not lead to complaints or failure to secure repeat custom.

In addition, if a business does not look hygienic and all the evidence suggests, that high standards of food hygiene and cleanliness are customer priorities, or if through poor word-of-mouth reports from friends or relatives the hygiene or cleanliness is questioned, customers may not even enter the premises. The catering and food retail trade should therefore be actively involved in measures to improve hygiene and cleanliness.

A sociologist (Finkelstein, 1989) proposed that an eating-place could evoke all manner of images, for example wealth, luxury and so on, represented through such things as the furnishing, the decor, the tableware and so on. These factors in turn are dominated by fashion. There is a correspondence, he suggested, in the minds of the customers between an atmosphere that is well constructed and the quality of the food. From the evidence outlined in this book an eating-place and indeed a food retail environment needs to create an image of cleanliness and having high standards of food hygiene and cleanliness.

Choosing a place to eat

It would also be sensible to ask the question whether poor standards of food hygiene and general cleanliness could dissuade potential customers. There has been plenty of research, undertaken some years ago, which generally indicates that food safety is not a factor which influences the public's choice when selecting an eating establishment. Lewis (1981) studied various advertising claims and assessed their importance to consumers and their effect on intention to go to a particular restaurant. He found that food quality was the most important factor affecting choice. There were other benefits or appeals to customers, but these depended on the type of restaurant and included atmosphere, price and menu variety.

Auty (1992) undertook a study to determine consumers' perceptions of restaurants and to investigate the way that they select an eating-place. Her study also included reasons for eating out to investigate if the occasion affected choice variables. Food type and food quality were the most frequently cited choice variables, regardless of the occasion for eating out, but image and atmosphere or style are critical in the final choice between restaurants that serve similar quality and type of food. However, her research did not indicate food hygiene as a major factor which influences the public's choice when selecting an eating-place.

The results of the author's research study broadly support Auty's findings. Food hygiene only features in the choice of an eating establishment when there was a recommendation from friends. The general consensus of opinion of those interviewed is that they would be influenced by what their friends tell them. However, several interviewees qualified what they said by adding that they found negative recommendations, ie not to visit a particular premises, which are also more likely to include food hygiene and cleanliness matters, far more powerful than a positive recommendation, as this respondent reported:

> I take far more notice of a warning than a recommendation, because if they've had a really bad experience then I'd avoid it. (Male: 16 – 24)

If you go out to eat and enjoy the experience you are unlikely to say to people you must go to this restaurant because it is clean and hygienic. But it would not be uncommon to say to friends and relatives you do not want to go to that eating-place because it is dirty! The professional group generally concurred with this view. The following quote summarises the position:

> People in my experience recommend you go to a place on the quality of the food or the price, not very often because it's clean. However, they may recommend you don't go to a place because it's dirty or the staff are filthy. In my book negative recommendations, ie don't go somewhere are far more valuable. (Catering professional)

Where the results of the author's research do conflict with Auty's findings is that the final decision to support a particular premises can be changed by the condition of the outside of the premises and by the standards of food hygiene and cleanliness inside. This is important information for the food industry because their attention should be applied to the conditions both immediately outside the business and inside because of the message that those conditions are portraying to potential customers. This view is summarised by these two quotes:

> I suppose a lack of care and attention. Too busy to get the little things right, and yet here I am, a potential customer that wants

'The final decision to support a particular premises can be changed by the condition of the outside of the premises and by the standards of food hygiene and cleanliness inside.'

to pay for a meal, put off before I get through the door. Or on my guard so that if I do go in, I'm already looking for other things which may not be right. It's almost a kind of game of 'spot the problem'. (Female: 16 – 24)

... only the other day I saw a menu outside a place which looked as if it had been in the container for donkey's years, in fact the sun had almost bleached the writing off the page. Clearly it had been neglected by the management, who had forgotten it or couldn't be bothered to change it. Lack of attention to detail you see, but it sends out negative messages. (Catering professional)

Poor control of such matters will be perceived as poor management in other aspects of the business, including standards of food hygiene and general cleanliness. In addition the initial image created inside the premises should be one that indicates food hygiene and cleanliness are taken seriously and managed properly. The following quote illustrates the position:

The emphasis in most eating-places will be on front of house, the bits the customers see. Everyone will go to the eating area, a good percentage will use the toilets, but no one will go into the kitchen. So if the standards have slipped in the public areas where they are on show, trying to impress you, it begs the question how far have the standards slipped behind the scenes? (Male: 25 – 34)

Do awards make a difference?

The answer to this question is not as straightforward as you may imagine. It would appear that generally the public consider awards to be positive and respondents to the research study said that given a choice between two similar establishments, the one holding the award would be more likely to attract their custom than the one not.

However, the awarding body was important. The public would appear to be reassured if the organisation making the awards was one that they had heard of, or recognised.

Interestingly the professionals were more sceptical about awards generally.

First they considered that the majority were issued for facilities present in a place or for the quality of the food, not for the standards of food hygiene. Secondly the date of issue of the award was important to the professionals — they considered that if an award was too old then standards may have slipped in the intervening period. Despite this rather cautious response there was a generally held view that a place holding an award had been able to achieve the criteria set for the achievement and this in itself, indicates that a premises may be better managed then those that have no awards, as this professional stated:

> ... places that get awards have at least been able to achieve those award standards. So I would still say they are likely to be better managed than ones without an award. (Environmental health professional)

One note of caution was issued by the professionals to the public, that just because a place has gained an award customers should not assume that the standards of food hygiene will be high. Customers should still be aware and alert to what is going on in the establishment, as this catering professional highlighted:

> The main thing is to go in with your eyes open, don't think just because a place has an award everything is brilliant. (Catering professional)

In essence, though, gaining awards is a positive thing and customers are more likely to support your establishment rather than an equivalent place that has no award. Choose to enter for awards that are granted by well-known organisations. Also you need to investigate how much the providers market and promote their awards to the public.

Some local authorities offer awards, under a variety of titles, for businesses that offer their customers high standards of food hygiene. Do think about the title of the award, though, because one called a 'Clean Food Award' carries an image of sterile tasteless food. If this is the case in your area, then try and persuade your local authority to reconsider the name of it.

The other thing to be aware of is that, if you have an award for food hygiene standards, possibly from your local authority, then you will raise the expectations of your customers. You are almost saying to them, 'we take food hygiene seriously and you can expect high standards here'. Customers are likely to be even more intolerant than usual of poor standards of food hygiene and general cleanliness.

Will a customer complain?

The majority of disgruntled customers are unlikely to complain. They do not find it easy – indeed, their preferred course of action, where a problem is encountered or where the service falls below that expected is to depart and not return, leaving the owner unaware of any perceived shortcomings. As these customers stated:

> I don't complain very much, I don't find it easy. It would have to be pretty bad. I tend to be put off and think I'm not coming back here. (Male: 35 – 44)

> I'd probably put up with what I saw, because I don't like complaining, I don't find it easy. I tend to grumble to whomever I'm with and then decide not to come back there again. (Female: 55 – 64)

> We should complain more than we do. But we don't like to upset people, I suppose that's the main reason. But I do think we should complain more. I suppose we get the standards we deserve. (Female: over 75)

This evidence was supported by the Food Standards Agency's *Consumer Attitudes to Food Standards* (2002a) which reported that the majority of consumers who experience problems or have concerns about hygiene in a variety of food outlets would not report their concerns to anyone in that business. Indeed, many claimed that they would vote with their feet by no longer using that outlet.

Interestingly, evidence provided by Leighton and Bent (1997) suggested that a business that trains it staff to deal with complaints effectively could gain a competitive advantage. The key message from this is for businesses to take steps to make it easy as possible for customers to voice their concerns. This may be achieved by increasing contact between staff and customers or by the use of easy to complete comment cards. If no action is taken then the evidence suggests that customers will be lost, proprietors will never know why, and the cycle will continue.

It may be a cliché but it would seem to be very appropriate: you are unlikely to get a second chance to make a good first impression.

'You are unlikely to get a second chance to make a good first impression.'

Chapter 3
The local authority perspective

Do the public know enough?

A book about public perceptions of food hygiene would not be complete without some discussion about how the public perceive the enforcers and also the local authority's role in enforcing food hygiene standards. To a certain extent the public's perception of the enforcers is shaped and influenced by many factors, just as the expectations about food hygiene standards in any eating-place are influenced by many factors.

The performance and levels of satisfaction generally with a local authority may be influenced by aspects of their work where that local authority are in direct contact with the public. For example, the cleanliness of the streets, satisfaction rates with the refuse collection service and the profile of the local authority in the local media will all have an influence in the public's mind as to how that local authority is performing.

This is very similar to the notion, which is explored in this book, that customers will transfer in their minds performance in one area to performance in another. Just as, for example, if the state of the toilets in a restaurant leaves a lot to be desired, then the customer using that toilet will assume that the kitchen too will be dirty and poorly managed. So if the local authority in any area has a poor public image because customers are not happy about the refuse service they receive, then they are likely to think that the food safety enforcement regime operated by that local authority is also poorly managed and not very effective.

Ask many people of a certain age to describe an environmental health practitioner and for many his or her thoughts will immediately turn to the most popular portrayal ever of a 'public health inspector' – Mr Carnegie (BBC, 1979). This was the grey suited official, totally lacking a sense of humour, who was unfortunate enough to visit 'Fawlty Towers' owned and run by one Basil Fawlty (John Cleese), ably assisted by his long suffering wife Sybil (Prunella Scales). The programme conjured up an image of an all-powerful, hard-nosed inspector who could, with one appearance, throw the entire establishment into blind panic.

This image has been reinforced over the years by appearances of environmental health practitioners in such popular soaps as *EastEnders*, *Coronation Street* and *Neighbours*, always portrayed as surly individuals who have the power to close a business down at the first sign of an infringement of the law. These are all images built up over time of a profession that the vast majority of members of the public are unlikely to meet.

Some of the most common questions I get asked during presentations to public audiences are: Do local authorities warn the businesses that they are going to inspect? How often do local authorities inspect food businesses? And is it easy to close a dirty food business down? In addition, it is clear from the discussions which follow that most members of the public believe that the powers of an environmental health practitioner are far greater than they actually are.

I think that many local authorities can be criticised for not informing the public enough about their role in protecting food safety and for not explaining how the various laws are enforced in relation to food safety.

The Food Safety Act 1990 and associated guidelines are designed to protect public health, but as one catering professional stated during the research:

> **'Most members of the public believe that the powers of an environmental health practitioner are far greater than they actually are.'**

... the law is very weak and most businesses can get away with fairly low standards and still comply with the law, or should I say avoid prosecution. (Catering professional)

As you will see below, this may be due to the way that the law is enforced rather than the law itself being weak.

By appointment

One area where it is considered there will be increasing discussion and debate is whether enforcement officers should make appointments to carry out food hygiene inspections. At the moment it would probably be accurate to say that the majority of inspections are made unannounced. However, there are certain occasions when appointments would be made, for example if it was necessary to see the manager of a very large establishment who is usually unavailable, or access was difficult due to irregular opening hours, or where the owner is rarely at the business and there would appear to be no one willing to take responsibility, and so on.

However, it could be argued that the unannounced visit is becoming more and more unfair on businesses. The requirements of the law and inspections are increasingly focusing on risk and there is a need to examine records, policies and procedures, all of which demand management time. To arrive at a business unannounced and expect immediate attention and time could be viewed as unreasonable these days.

This view, though, has to be tempered against a need to see how the business is run on a day-to-day basis, not spruced up for an inspection. It also cannot be forgotten that the reason for the rules and regulations are to protect the consumer and public health. Guidance issued to local authorities, which they must have regard to, states that as a general rule inspections shall be carried out without prior warning (Ministry of Agriculture, Fisheries and Food et al. 1991). The guidance does go on to state that there will be circumstances when it may be advantageous to give advance notice, but officers should exercise discretion guided by the overriding aim of ensuring compliance with food legislation. Certainly the tone of the questions I get asked by the public, to which I referred earlier, is one where it is expected that no warning of a visit will be given and I think there would be both surprise and dismay if an appointment were made.

The frequency of visits are also determined by the risk that any business poses to the public. The type of food sold, the type of preparation, to whom the food is sold, the risk to the public by non-compliance with the law, the confidence in the management of the business to effectively control food safety and the state of the structure of the building are all taken into account. The inspecting officer will give each business inspected a score based upon what is found and witnessed and this score determines the frequency of visits. All the criteria for scoring and the frequency of visits are laid down in a Code of Practice (Food Standards Agency, 2000). Depending upon the score given to a business, visits will take place between every six months for the highest scoring business to every five years for the business scoring the least.

Enforcement matters

Since the introduction of the Food Safety Act 1990 enforcement of the law has become an issue of interest in itself. Back in 1991 the Audit Commission considered that:

There was a growing argument for the effectiveness of rigorous enforcement, often by prosecution at an early stage.

The Commission's view was that a determined prosecution strategy also had considerable merit in management terms being clear-cut and easy to communicate. However, since then there has been a shift in emphasis.

Successive governments have encouraged local authorities to take a more laissez-faire approach to the law and to focus on risk to health when deciding upon action to be taken in any situation. It is not surprising therefore that the number of 'Improvement Notices' served under the Food Safety Act 1990 has fallen sharply. In 1992, 41,641 establishments were subject to 'Improvement Notices'; by 1997 this total had fallen to 3,399 (Ministry of Agriculture, Fisheries and Food, 1997), and by 2000 the numbers remained very low at 4,247 (Food Standards Agency, 2002b), when compared with the early 1990s. This is despite the fact that the Food Standards Agency reported that of the 385,507 food premises inspected by food enforcement officers, 174,417 had failed to comply with food law in some way (Food Standards Agency, 2002b).

The background to this change of direction in enforcement was politically motivated. In the beginning, following the enactment of the Food Safety Act 1990, the strict enforcement regime was aimed at placating public opinion. Following a number of food scares, most notably the Salmonella in eggs problem, the government had to be seen to be doing something. But as time moved on there were a number of government initiatives aimed at reducing 'red tape' and a culture of working with and assisting business to comply with the law developed and became popular.

There was a time in the mid-1990s when it was commonplace to see in newspapers articles about over-zealous enforcement. A book was published entitled: The Mad Officials (Booker and North, 1994) which highlighted examples of the damage done to industry and individual businesses by new regulations imposed by Europe and the way the law was being enforced locally. Many of the examples used in the book and in the book's authors' regular feature articles in the Daily and Sunday Telegraph newspapers were the subject of a document produced by the Local Authorities Coordinating Body on Food and Trading Standards (1994). The document provided a platform for the authorities concerned to reply to some of the cases highlighted in the articles and filled in the background.

There then followed a number of incidents involving food, most notably the Bovine Spongiform Encephalopathy (BSE) problems and the E. coli 0157 outbreak in Lanarkshire in Scotland. These rocked public confidence in the safety of food and the ability of the government and the food industry to control food safety, so much so that food safety became an issue in the 1997 General Election.

New Labour (1997) in their manifesto promised to establish an independent Food Standards Agency. Below is an extract from that manifesto:

> The £3.5 billion BSE crisis and the E. coli outbreak, which resulted in serious loss of life, have made unanswerable the case for the independent agency we have proposed.

The fact that New Labour won the 1997 General Election is history and details of the proposed Food Standards Agency emerged.

The government published a White Paper which contained proposals for the new Agency (Ministry of Agriculture, Fisheries and Food, 1998). As that White Paper made clear, food safety is an issue which concerns every man, woman and child in this country. The government believed that the creation of a Food Standards Agency would put an end to the climate of confusion and suspicion which resulted from the way that food safety and standards issues had been handled in the past. Most notabley was the fact that the same Ministry had been responsible both for promoting food safety and standards issues and for the industry which produces the food.

Although a very simplified version of events has been given above, it shows that the power of the consumer and public opinion, mixed with a political will, can bring about fundamental changes.

The Food Standards Agency was created in April 2000 and has a clear focus, according to the Food Standards Act 1999, that focus being to protect public health and consumers' interests in relation to food. Since its inception the Food Standards Agency has operated under three guiding principles according to the Agency's Strategic Plan (2001b):

- to put consumers first;
- being open and accessible;
- being an independent voice.

The Strategic Plan went on to state a number of priorities that the Agency wants to achieve in relation to improving food safety and to make it possible for people to choose a healthy diet. One of those priorities relates to the issue of improving enforcement. The Agency views effective enforcement of food law as essential to protecting consumers and the Strategic Plan listed four issues it wants to progress:

- To improve the effectiveness of local authority and Meat Hygiene Service enforcement;
- To ensure proportionate and more consistent enforcement;
- To improve transparency of enforcement arrangements for stakeholders;
- To promote the wider implementation of risk-based systems for improving safety standards across the food chain.

To increase openness all local authorities should now have an enforcement policy. This document, which is available to businesses and the public, spells out the enforcement options available to the authority and that these options should be instigated in a stepped approach depending upon risk. The purpose of the policy is to encourage a consistent and open approach, which is proportionate to the risk.

The Food Standards Agency has also produced a document called *The Framework Agreement on Local Authority Food Law Enforcement* (2001a). This document sets out the expectations of the Food Standards Agency in relation to what all local authorities should be producing in the form of auditable policies and procedures. The agreement also requires local authorities to make regular returns to the Food Standards Agency listing enforcement activity. By this means the Agency can keep a better watch on what is going on in the country, and monitor the performance of all local authorities, and of course publish the results of any audits and returns.

What the future may hold

There will almost certainly be a new set of general food hygiene regulations in the not too distant future which will combine a number of existing regulations. They are also likely to contain a requirement for some written form of hazard analysis, focusing the attention of proprietors of food businesses on the hazards to food safety. A written document and records will make it a lot easier to audit than the current arrangements.

> **'We live in an age of consumer power when the voice of the consumer must be heard; such an approach will play an increasing part in the way policy is informed.'**

We live in an age of consumer power when the voice of the consumer must be heard; such an approach will play an increasing part in the way policy is informed. The way things stand at the moment if anyone wants to go out to eat or to hire an outside catering contractor for a function, for example a birthday party or a wedding, then that person has no way of knowing how good or bad in relation to food hygiene that provider is. They can see if the business is registered with the local authority, providing that, in the case of an outside caterer, the business operates relatively frequently, but the customers will not know the standards of that business as assessed by the local authority. So in theory an eating-place or an outside caterer – or retailer for that matter – could be weeks away from being prosecuted or be subject to other enforcement action, but the public would not be aware of it.

This raises a whole host of questions as to whether the public should be told these facts. Should, for example, the results of the last local authority inspection be available to members of the public, perhaps on the Internet? Should local authorities award scores to businesses so the public could assess the standards based upon those scores? Should there be some national award scheme for eating-places and food retailers? Of course for every question or option for action there are an equal number of advantages and drawbacks.

If an award is granted how could it be removed if standards fall? It is easy to give an award but never quite so easy to remove it. If the results of a food hygiene inspection are to be made available to the public, what happens if the proprietor fundamentally disagrees with the report? What facilities will exist for an appeal? Standards of food hygiene and general cleanliness in a business can either fall or improve dramatically between inspections. Would the public understand the complexities of the law and be able to relate that to risk?

None of these problems are insurmountable, but they will need careful thought. It is considered, however, that some form of action will be taken in due course to enlighten customers more about the standards of food hygiene and general cleanliness in any eating-place or food retail outlet.

Chapter 4
Outside the business

Imagine that you are going out to eat or wish to buy some food. As you move closer to your chosen hostelry or shop, the area set aside for rubbish catches your eye, maybe the route taken from your car leads you past the refuse area. If it is clean and tidy and looks well managed you may not even notice it. But if it is untidy, maybe the bin lids are not closed properly or there is a large build-up of refuse sacks thrown untidily in a heap with one or two leaking their contents, you probably will notice it, you may even draw it to the attention of anyone you are with. Perhaps if your trip out is in the summer you may notice a slight odour or be warding off an invasion of flies.

There is a danger then that you will have doubts about the effectiveness of the management to control the business effectively. You may start to think whether this lack of care and attention will be present inside the premises. If you had these thoughts you would not be alone – most people would probably think the same.

Although knowledge of food hygiene informs us that the outside of most places has little impact on the food hygiene and cleanliness inside, it cannot be ignored that people transfer the evidence provided by one clue onto another aspect of the business. Although there may be no rhyme or reason why; poor management of one area of a business will be viewed as poor management of another.

Compared to other criteria, the outside of the business is lower down the list of priorities than others for the public, when it comes to assessing the standards of food hygiene. However, there is no doubt that an initial assessment of a business can start for many outside. If there are poor conditions in existence and things do not look cared for, then a customer's decision to go ahead with choosing the establishment might be affected. The research highlighted that the majority of people would move on; others may still go ahead but would be wary or on their guard. The professional group agreed with the public, as this statement explains:

If I wasn't desperate to eat there and then, and I had the choice, I would go somewhere else. (Catering professional)

> **'Although there may be no rhyme or reason why; poor management of one area of a business will be viewed as poor management of another.'**

The professional group also claimed to do what the general public do and transfer the evidence given by one clue onto another aspect of the business. This quote by a teacher explains:

> It tells me that they are not taking a pride in their establishment and I wouldn't want to go in, because it tells me that they probably don't take a pride in their food. (Teaching professional)

As potential customers walk towards a business or as they cross the car park, consider what the state of the rubbish area is saying to those potential customers, as discussed earlier. The evidence from the research suggests that they may well glance at it – indeed the fact the rubbish areas look clean and tidy was their most important clue, outside, to a well-run business. The professional group agreed with this assessment too. They concurred that of all the clues outside, the management of waste is one of the most reliable, although low down on the list of priorities when compared to other factors.

Always strive therefore to have a clean and tidy waste area and avoid overflowing bins. If there is a need for extra waste sacks outside, then ensure that they are stacked tidily and are not broken open.

Whether the approach to the business taken by potential customers is directly off the pavement or via a car park, it should be clean and tidy and look inviting. The message should be, 'you can have confidence in us to get things right'.

In summary, there should be nothing which might suggest to potential customers, at this early stage of the service encounter any cause for concern or which might attract their attention and give out a negative message.

Chapter 5
Inside the business

Upon entering any premises, whether it is a restaurant, pub or food shop, all of us form an impression very quickly. This impression is built up by several factors including the decor, the furnishings, the lighting, the table settings, the smell, the attitude and dress of the staff and so on. As Lancaster and Massingham (1993) explained, we select, organise and interpret the stimuli put before us. We also draw upon our previous experiences and expectations.

Evidence would suggest that levels of cleanliness and food hygiene are to a certain extent taken for granted as being satisfactory – after all, it is a food business! But – and it is a big but – if an impression is created of lack of cleanliness and untidiness then those issues become a focus of attention, and like the subjects of the previous and following chapters, customers become motivated to look deeper than first impressions. They may become wary and many will leave without an explanation, leading to lost customers and lost income.

The issue of cleanliness is an important one to the public. They view the state of cleanliness of a premises and items within it as providing vital clues about the standards of food hygiene in those premises. The issue of cleanliness included items such as equipment, food service areas and surfaces, bar areas, serving dishes, floors and carpets, walls, ceilings, windows and curtains.

Interestingly the professional group cautioned the public about focusing their attention on one object or area. They claimed it would be wrong for a customer to base their whole judgement of a place on one clue alone. They should be looking for a broader picture of the standards by looking at several clues. This statement by an environmental health professional summarises the view:

> I think you can pick up clues which give an indication about the standards, but I don't think you can rely or base your whole judgement on just one or two clues. You need to look at the broader picture presented by several indicators. (Environmental health professional)

Although cleanliness is viewed as important by customers, and they clearly equate it with high standards of food hygiene, to the owner or manager of an eating place or food shop, things are not always that straightforward. They will know that superficial cleanliness can be deceptive. A food surface can

look clean, but may not be bacteriologically clean. In looking at the many definitions of food hygiene which exist, cleanliness is seen as a contributory factor to food hygiene, not the sole factor.

In many eating-places the kitchens are clearly visible to customers, which seems to inspire confidence, especially if they are clean and look tidy. Indeed a visible kitchen puts a greater onus on the managers and staff to keep these areas clean and tidy. In most food shops, areas where 'open' food is handled like delicatessens, meat and fish counters and bakeries are visible to customers and care must be taken to keep these areas clean and tidy too, to make them look inviting and encourage people to buy.

However, there are some eating-places where customers cannot readily see the kitchens. In these cases the majority of the public find it important to try and get a glimpse into the food preparation areas where this is possible, perhaps as doors swing open. Clearly, natural curiosity gets the better of them. The professional group backed this inquisitiveness; they included it under the umbrella of hidden clues, as this catering professional explains:

> It is a good thing to look in the doors if you can see [the kitchen]. Look to see that the kitchen is not cluttered, that the floor is clean and there is a general feeling of cleanliness about the place, that everything looks ordered and well run and that the staff look properly dressed with relatively clean overalls and hats. It's difficult in those few seconds, but you may be able to get a feel of the place and that's reassuring. (Catering professional)

As an environmental health practitioner, I am often asked by members of the public whether they have a right to look in the kitchen of any restaurant. Some caterers also ask me whether they have a right to refuse entry to a customer wishing to see the kitchen. The answer is 'no', the customer does not have a right to see the kitchen, and 'yes', as a caterer you have no obligation to show a customer the kitchen. There is a paradox here though. By refusing to let a customer see the kitchen, are you by your refusal appearing to hide something? But as an environmental health practitioner I would not be happy for customers to wander into the kitchen on the grounds that they might unwittingly contaminate food and represent a risk in terms of health and safety both to themselves and employees.

The whole issue of awards and the display of certificates is an interesting one which has already been discussed. The public generally consider awards to be positive and support them, and premises holding awards are more likely to attract customers than those that do not where there is a choice. However, the awarding body was important to the public; they felt reassured if the organisation making the awards was one that they had heard of and recognised.

In respect of training certificates in food hygiene, the message from the public is the same. Seeing certificates sends out positive messages and the public like to see them. But three words of caution: first, keep the certificates up to date – certificates that are too old send out messages that the staff's knowledge is out of date. Second, make sure that the certificates apply to staff that are still employed by the business. Third, and most importantly, you are drawing customers' attention to the fact that the staff in the place have been trained in food hygiene. While this is positive, it may heighten their awareness of the topic and then they are likely to be less forgiving if they see minor problems, especially with regard to poor personal hygiene.

Both animals and insects are also of interest to the public and the fact that flies are kept away from food was one of the highest rated clues cited by members of the public when assessing the standards of food hygiene. Proprietors of food businesses then should take steps to prevent flies from gaining access to places where food is served, prepared, handled or sold. Clearly a fly loitering with intent around a food service area will attract customers' attention in a very negative way.

Despite being a nation of animal lovers, pet animals present in an eating-place send out a negative signal to most customers too, especially cats because of their tendency to climb onto things and increase the risk of contamination. These two statements summarise the views taken by the majority:

I don't like to see animals wandering around and sitting on tables or chairs when food is being served. This is a regular problem in public houses. (Female: 45 – 54)

Are there any pets running around the place, especially cats that tend to climb on everything. (Male: 35 – 44)

As an Environmental health practitioner I always find it amusing when inspecting a premises and half way through that inspection into the kitchen wanders the family dog. The proprietor usually panics and talks to the dog as if it should recognise a health inspector at 40 paces and says something like: 'you know you're not allowed in here – get out!' as it is ushered from the food handling area. Of course the poor dog normally looks totally bewildered as it was heading for its water bowl 'invisibly' sited near to the refrigerator!

It would be wrong before leaving the area of the interior of the premises not to mention the toilets, because the research generated a lot of comment and clues relating to them. The aspects sought out by the public were the general cleanliness of the whole toilet area, the pans and the wash hand basins adequate amounts of toilet paper, good supplies of soap, the availability of hand drying materials or facilities, and hot and cold water.

There is a view, mentioned earlier, in this book (and it will be again), that poor standards experienced in one aspect of the business equals the presence of poor standards elsewhere, including standards of food hygiene. The toilets are no exception. Take these three comments as an example, and they are not uncommon:

What are the toilets like? If they are bad, what is the kitchen like? (Male: 65 – 74)

If the toilets are not clean, then the standards are low, meaning food preparation areas are unclean too. (Female: 35 – 44)

The emphasis in most eating-places will be on the front of house, the bits the customers see. Everyone will go to the eating area, a good percentage will use the toilets, but no one will go to into the kitchens. So if the standards have slipped in the public areas, where they are on show trying to impress you, how far have the standards slipped behind the scenes? (Male: 25 – 34)

The professionals agreed with the public's view too, especially the catering professional cohort who drew strong links. These two statements illustrate the position:

> 'If the standards have slipped in the public areas, where they are on show trying to impress you, how far have the standards slipped behind the scenes?'

> Unsatisfactory toilets, in a poor state of repair and cleanliness are an indication of the lack of importance that the management place upon hygiene. This may be reflected in other public areas and suspected in the kitchens. (Catering professional)

> You tend to think that if they can't keep the toilets clean you wonder what else is not clean. I think it's a management link. Both areas need to be managed well in a catering establishment and if one isn't right, what else isn't right? (Catering professional)

The environmental health professionals drew links too:

> If I inspect the public toilets before I inspect the kitchen and they aren't very good, then I would start to anticipate that the kitchen isn't very good either. (Environmental health professional)

On a personal note, I have seen many signs in toilets stating that they are regularly checked for cleanliness. The notices go on to state who customers should inform if the toilets are not in the condition that they would want to find them. In addition I have seen in some places a board on which staff write the times that the toilets have been checked and/or cleaned. This too is positive, provided that the spaces have been properly filled in and of course the toilets are clean and well stocked with supplies of soap, toilet paper, towels, etc. I remember on one occasion seeing one of these notices proudly stating that the facilities were inspected and cleaned every two hours, but there was no sign on the log/board provided, where staff initial to register that this had been done, that the toilets had been examined, let alone cleaned, for a day and a half! Incidentally they looked like they hadn't been attended to as well!

Chapter 6
Staff working in the business

Included under this heading are all the influences that staff can have on the business as perceived by customers. The clues given by members of the public and professionals alike were diverse in nature and content and covered such issues as habits, clothing, cleanliness, jewellery, impressions, tasks undertaken, state of health and attitude.

There is no doubt that staff working in any food business can put people off their food or indeed continuing with their custom by their actions, behaviour and the way that they dress. This quote from a member of the public illustrates the view:

> We'd just sat down and there was this lad behind the counter, it was a burger type place and I saw him pick his nose. I thought this is it and we didn't even stop for a coffee. (Female: 55 – 64)

I recall visiting a baker's shop one Saturday afternoon, near to where I live, to buy two small cakes. On entering the shop I noticed I was the only customer and as I made my way to the service counter I also noticed that the lady serving was just recovering from what must have been a fit of sneezing. The tissue with which she was very vigorously blowing and wiping her nose was getting smaller as she folded it over. The thought of *Staphylococcus aureus* bacteria being transferred onto her hands and then onto my food didn't even register; I was more concerned with mucous getting on to my cakes. Then I was asked what I would like as this damp tissue was neatly pushed into her overall pocket. Pausing for a few moments, I said: 'would you mind washing your hands first'. The reaction I got was tinged with embarrassment, but the lady did wash her hands, very much under an unsaid protest, and I was served with my cakes in a very customer unfriendly way. The whole encounter was not pleasant for either of us. I left the shop with the two cakes that I did not feel like consuming and I haven't returned to that shop since. On reflection how different the whole outcome would have been if before I had been served the lady had said to me: 'I'm just going to rinse my hands first before I serve you'. Not only would my fears about mucous on my food have been allayed, but I would have left the shop with a view that food hygiene is important to that business and I definitely would have returned.

The point can be further illustrated by an experience I encountered (see page 39).

That story leads the discussion onto habits, practices and personal hygiene generally. Certainly staff coughing and sneezing over food is a major turn off for customers and professionals alike. If the same staff have cause to blow their nose they should be seen to wash their hands as well.

Customers are also upset if they see staff tasting food by using fingers and licking them or using a spoon which is returned to the dish. Other habits like fiddling with the hair, touching the nose or whatever are also seen as no go areas. Yet both these habits are commonplace and, because they are habits, people do not realise that they are doing it. This is where both staff training and good supervision are important.

Hands too are a big aspect of personal hygiene which is important to customers. Hands should be clean as should fingernails and if possible staff should be seen to wash their hands occasionally but especially in between different tasks. Any cuts or abrasions on the hands or forearms should be covered with coloured waterproof dressings because this, again, is an outward show of care and attention to detail, apart from also being a legal requirement.

The clothing and look of the staff are important. Staff should look clean and smart and be wearing clean and appropriate protective work clothing

or uniforms. The wearing of hats while food is being prepared or cooked by those who are doing those tasks was highlighted as good to see. Hair too should be clean and tidy and if the hair is long it should be tied back. A number of members of the public said that it was important for staff to look smart and be well presented, whatever their role or function.

I recall one incident that illustrates a point, when I recently went to buy some cakes from a local baker. I joined the queue of other customers and noticed that 'Saturday girls' were serving us all. While in the queue I acknowledged the manageress on duty. It so happened that she knew me and that I was an environmental health practitioner. I noticed that she very hastily beckoned one of the young staff over to her and whispered something in her ear. This girl then promptly walked behind the other girl who was about to serve me and in a very unsubtle way said into her ear: 'Use the tongs on this one!' 'You what?' came the reply, and the other girl repeated the manageress's message even louder. 'Use the tongs on this one!' Unfortunately they then had to hunt down the tongs. The manageress looked at me rather sheepishly and said: 'They do let you down, don't they?' While I was very flattered to receive this VIP treatment, all customers should be served cakes by the use of tongs rather than bare hands.

On one occasion I remember going to have coffee on a Saturday morning in a large department store. I joined the queue, along with other customers, placing my tray on the tray slide and moving along as customers up ahead were being provided with their hot drinks. I overheard a couple talking a few ahead of me in the queue, referring to the young man who was serving. As I moved closer to the hot drinks service area I could see the problem. The young man, unfortunately for him and us as customers, had an irritating and regular cough. In between each cup of hot drink served, he was coughing into his hand and then proceeded to handle every cup by the rim with the hand that had just been coughed into. Now there was probably no risk to our health, as customers in any way. But the practice was upsetting customers and I found it aesthetically undesirable. So rather than confront this young man in front of other customers which I am sure would have embarrassed him and probably me, I stepped out of the queue and went to speak to one of the supervisors. The supervisor was apologetic and did immediately sort the issue out by replacing the young man doing the job. This small incident did make me wonder though, if anyone had decided to go elsewhere for his or her morning refreshments?

... if I thought their overalls were dirty or if they were unshaven and dirty looking then it would put me off, as that's the first impression of who is going to be preparing my meal. If they come in looking good and clean then it would boost your confidence about how the food is going to be prepared. (Male: 16 – 24)

The way in which food is served by staff can have an impact on people and can affect the way in which they view a business. While the use of tongs, slices, spoons and other utensils for the serving of food is important, the main thing is that staff do not touch the food as they serve it. This care when serving food also goes for the way in which cutlery, crockery and glassware are handled. The public are quite clear that these items should never be held or touched on their rim or any part coming into contact with the customer's mouth.

The general attitude of staff also brought forth some clues that the public use to assess businesses. Many members of the public consider that a 'couldn't care less attitude' demonstrated by staff, whether it was when serving food, cleaning tables or in their general dealings with customers, indicated that that negative attitude would be translated into all other areas of their work, including food hygiene and related duties. This view was strongly reflected by the professional cohort too.

Some members of the professional cohort went further and questioned the lack of professionalism by some in the catering trade who it was suggested gave the whole industry a bad name, as illustrated by this statement:

... some people who work in the catering trade portray both an attitude and actions as if food hygiene, including personal hygiene matters, are beneath them, as if they are not important. That sort of behaviour can give the whole premises a bad name. Linked to this is that sometimes you get management behaving as if the rules do not apply to them and they will wander into food service areas without any overalls on or just start serving, when clearly they haven't washed their hands or anything. (Catering professional)

Lastly under this heading of staff working in the premises comes the issue of training. Poor standards of personal hygiene, poor appearance and a

negative attitude could and do for many
Indicate a lack of staff training and
management control. The two are importantly
linked. Staff could be trained to a high level,
but if that training is not supported, reinforced
and encouraged by action in the workplace by
the management, then it is partly a waste of
time and money. The public tend to focus on the
display of training certificates as evidence of
staff training, although clearly by the other
clues stated, they also look for evidence of this

> 'Working with food in a public setting
> is like being on stage in front of an
> audience. That audience is the
> customers. They will be watching very
> critically and will act upon what they
> see by applauding a good
> performance, but will possibly leave
> and/or never return if the performance
> is poor.'

training being put into practice. The professional groups viewed staff
training as essential to the efficient running of a food business and the
maintenance of high standards of food hygiene.

The issue of the display of certificates was discussed in the previous chapter
(on matters inside the business) together with the importance of the
certificates applying to those still working in the business and the fact that
any certificates should be relevatively recent. The professional group went
on to state that staff should be judged on what they actually do, not what
certificates state they know. As this Environmental health professional
stated:

> Look to see what the staff do, because that's what counts in the end.
> (Environmental health professional)

To conclude, I consider it worth thinking of working with food in a public
setting as if one is on stage in front of an audience and that audience is the
customers. Customers will be watching the performance very critically and
will act upon what they see by applauding a good performance, but possibly
leave and/or never return if the performance is poor. It is unlikely, though,
that the applause will be heard! That applause is generally transferred into
satisfaction with the service and repeat custom.

Chapter 7
The table and the immediate environment

The public group consider that the table and the immediate environment provide the diner with vital clues as to the standards of food hygiene in any eating-place. On taking their place at a table a customer is staking out their territory and things become, albeit temporarily, their property. This is interestingly evidenced by a change in language and terms used. For example, customers will refer to the toilets, the lounge, the menu and so on in neutral terms. But as soon as they are allocated a table, words like my table, my cutlery, and my chair creep into the vocabulary. As we know, everything in any eating establishment belongs in some way to that business, but customers suddenly pretend that a small part of that business belongs to them. They become very territorial and because of this the evidence suggests that they appear to increase the expected standards of cleanliness in particular. Certainly, the level of importance that the public attached to the clues in this aspect of the service encounter was generally very high.

All the evidence suggests that customers do not want to be reminded of who sat at the table before them or that the eating equipment was someone else's a few moments before. There would appear to be an unspoken trust that all steps have been taken to remove evidence that the most intimate eating equipment that a customer is going to use is clean.

Once seated at a table the customer has a chance to, and clearly does, examine in close detail the standards of food hygiene in that small part of the establishment and the management of them. For many, this will be the first opportunity to undertake such a close assessment in any detail. Up to this point the picture of the standards for many tend to be constructed of hastily formed impressions.

The standards as perceived by the customers, therefore, can be greatly enhanced by the images created at the table. The efforts to boost that image put in by management and staff can pay dividends. The factors included in this theme are therefore numerous and indicate what customers are looking at.

> 'Once seated at a table the customer has a chance to, and clearly does, examine in close detail the standards of food hygiene in that small part of the establishment.'

There should be no visible waste on the floor around or under the tables; this will include scraps of food and paper serviettes carelessly discarded by previous customers. Cleaning schemes should be employed so that all visible material is removed as quickly and as discreetly as possible. If this procedure is undertaken as soon as the table is vacated, the reason to everyone present and incoming customers becomes obvious. However, if this cleaning operation is left so that new customers are confronted with the waste, then the picture does not look so inviting.

The table itself should be clean and not sticky in anyway, and if tablecloths are used then they too should be clean, as should any serviettes provided. Other items on the table should also be clean, including ashtrays, salt and pepper containers and menus – indeed the public like to see both clean and stain-free menus. In addition ashtrays should not only be clean but be emptied regularly. Sauce bottles and relish containers for customer use should be clean and have no residue build-up around the neck or any other part of the container.

Trays used for and by customers should be clean and dry, so that the customer does not have to worry about any possibility of them being contaminated or reminded that someone else was using them a few moments previously.

Then we come to the cutlery, crockery and glassware. As you would expect, customers assume these items will be clean; however, the issue of cleanliness was further expanded and qualified. Customers do not wish to see watermarks on the cutlery or glassware, and in addition they expect the glassware to be sparkling. The crockery too should be chip and crack free according to the public.

In a busy eating-place with a high customer turnover, it is a challenge to maintain standards as if it was the first sitting of any meal session. However, the evidence points to the fact that keeping tables cleared and cleaned, including the floor underneath and around the tables and the chairs, enhances the image of the establishment considerably.

I recall visiting a roadside eatery recently for meal, to break rather a long journey I was making. As my wife and I walked into the restaurant we were confronted by a very untidy eating area, 13 out 26 tables contained the evidence of the previous customers and the floor was littered with paper serviettes and food scraps. Eventually we were shown to a table, which had to be cleared to let us sit down. As we were seated I noticed that part of the floor area, where children were entertained, was so littered with toys and debris that any customer walking through would have been at considerable risk of tripping over. There were only six other customers in the place and we specifically commented to a member of staff how busy they must have been, evidenced by the un-cleared tables, litter and debris. 'A steady trickle' came the reply, yet by the look of the place two coach loads of very messy customers must have just vacated the eatery. This was clearly not the case, indeed studying the staffs activities, four of them were on duty, demonstrated that they were more keen on talking amongst themselves than attending to their customers. The very laid back attitude of the staff did make us consider the levels of cleanliness in the cooking area and whether the food hygiene would be up to scratch, but hunger got the better of us. A visit to the toilets was a mistake too! Apart from having to employ my risk assessment skills to avoid probable infection, they looked as if they had not been attended to for a very long time, indeed the cleaning notice, which stated that they were inspected and cleaned every two hours had not been signed for over 24 hours! On returning home a letter was sent to the area office and a very plausible reason for our experience was given. But for my wife and I the damage had been done, and apart from telling many friends and people about the experience and using it in presentations, I have never revisited the restaurant, despite doing the same journey many times.

Chapter 8
Food and drink

The food and drink available in any public eating-place provide clear clues to members of the public about the standards of food hygiene in those premises. All the clues given by the public falling under this theme, bar one about the presentation of food, were assessed as 'important' or 'very important' on an importance scale. This topic therefore is a vital ingredient which helps customers to create a picture of the standards of food hygiene in a business.

The vast majority of clues in this theme can be subdivided into three categories: temperature, contamination, and freshness of food. Research undertaken by Roberts (1982) about the reasons for food poisoning occurring found that poor temperature control is a major contributory factor. Indeed top of Roberts' list was: 'food prepared too far in advance and stored at room temperature'.

The public it would seem are suspicious of food that is not refrigerated or kept hot. The temperature of cold meats and salad bars was of most concern and the public like to see these foods refrigerated. They also like to be sure that their food is cooked properly, right the way through, unless it is ordered otherwise. The professional cohort agreed with these views and the following statement reflects the general view held by the professionals:

> Hot food should be hot and cold food should be cold because it is at its most dangerous when its warm or at room temperature. All food should be cooked properly and hot right the way through, unless of course it has been ordered otherwise. (Catering professional)

No one would expect to discover that their food is contaminated, either with bacteria, which might make them ill, or with a physical object from whatever source. In many eating-places, nowhere can physical contamination be more visible than in salad stuffs which are particularly prone to contamination with insects or soil, and the fact that these should be well washed is one clue that the public claims to take account of.

It is important to the public that food on display is covered or at least protected from other customers so that the chances of it becoming contaminated are reduced to a minimum.

Freshness of food was an issue for members of the public; they appeared to be suspicious that lack of freshness masked further problems linked to the management of both food and the premises generally. As one member of the public stated:

> You wouldn't put lettuce like that on someone's plate if you were taking care. If it happens then I start to think that they don't take much care and what are other things like. Or if cucumber is dry on the cut slice, that indicates it's been around for some time and the same things happen, I start to worry about other things. (Female: 25 – 34)

The linkage between clues which has emerged in all the other themes was also evident in relation to packet foods which may have a date displayed on it. With this type of wrapped food the date provides a very clear clue about both the freshness of the food and the management of it, according to the public, as this statement shows:

> [about out of date food] I'd take it back if it was out of date. They should check these things and if they can't be bothered or they hope to get away with it then it doesn't say much for the management regime, does it? (Female: 55 – 64)

Linkages were also drawn in relation to other foods too:

> … I don't like to see skin formed on the top of bowls of salad cream, sauces, and mustards that kind of thing puts me off. It makes me question their management of the food generally. (Male: 55 – 64)

The topping up of food on displays, carveries, salad bars and the like was an issue which for many members of the public gave important clues about the standards of food hygiene set in many establishments. The common view was that if a dish of food on display was getting low then the whole dish should be changed, and not have the fresh food tipped on top of the old. This position was backed by most of the professional group, as summed up by this professional:

I remember on one occasion, as an environmental health practitioner, receiving several complaints about salad stuffs being sold from a supermarket delicatessen. The complaints related to an 'off' and 'fermenting' type of after-taste being experienced by the complainants. Upon investigation it was found that one of assistants working on the delicatessen counter was in the habit of constantly topping up the dishes of salad with fresh and never changing or washing out the display containers. The residue of food therefore in the bottom of the dishes, although constantly mixed with new, was old stock and was contaminating the new and turning it 'off' very quickly. Luckily for the customers the result was an 'off' taste and nothing more serious – it could have been food contaminated with pathogenic bacteria and it may have had the opportunity to grow, with serious consequences both for the customers and the supermarket.

Look to see how they manage the carvery or salad bar, do they top dishes up or change them. They should change the whole dish, not top it up. Is it looking neat and tidy and not like a bomb has hit it? (Catering professional)

Although the public claimed that the presentation of food on display was a clue by which to assess the standards of food hygiene in an establishment, the professional group did not all agree with this, especially where it related to presentation of food on the plate. This statement summarises the position:

I think presentation of food on the plate isn't really anything to do with food hygiene. If something is served to you swimming in grease that doesn't make it unhygienic. (Catering professional)

To conclude this chapter, there were members of the public, and no doubt the professionals, who claimed that they would use their knowledge of food hygiene and safety to good effect when eating out. They claimed that if they had any doubt about the standards of general cleanliness or food hygiene in an establishment then they would take care with their choice of food. They would avoid choosing foods which might present a higher risk of food poisoning. The more comfortable they felt about the standards, the more adventurous they might be with their selections off the menu. This statement illustrates the point:

> ... seafood especially shellfish. I wouldn't eat them in a restaurant that I didn't feel 100 per cent happy with, I'd stick to something plainer. The more confidence I have the more adventurous I become. I always do that even in sandwich bars and the fillings I choose.
> (Female: 35 – 44)

Chapter 9
Closing comments

If there is one thread which runs through the contents of this book in terms of the clues which the public claim to look for and which links them all together then that is management. Rightly or wrongly the majority of problems that occur in a food premises, whether it is a restaurant, hotel, pub, café, take-away or shop, as far as both the public and professionals are concerned, are down to poor management. While there may be many calls on valuable management time and from a lot of sources, it is unfortunate that customers view hygiene and cleanliness problems, relating to a particular business, quite often as management's own making. Those customers will not be that forgiving of poor standards. The following three statements from the research reflect this view whether it is problem with the staff:

> At the end of the day it all comes down to management. They are in-charge of the staff and the responsibility stops with them and if the staff aren't keeping up the required standards then the management should put things right by getting staff who will do the job.
> (Male: 25 – 34)

or with the premises:

> It concerns me very much that they are interlinked. Any form of cleanliness around the premises speaks a lot for the management of the premises in general. If the toilets are not up to scratch it means to me that the management is not to scratch. They should be checking things like that. (Female: 55 – 64)

or the food:

> [About out of date food] I'd take it back if it was out of date. They should check these things and if they can't be both bothered or they hope to get away with it, then it doesn't say much for the management regime, does it? (Female: 55 – 64)

Some of the clues cited in this book do not appear on first examination to have much to do with either food hygiene or the standards of cleanliness, but they are claimed to be used as clues to those standards by members of the public and therefore customers or potential customers. There would appear to be a form of transference in people's minds, that if they see or experience something in one area of a business they make assumptions about things in other areas of the business that can and cannot necessarily be seen.

What is clear is that, although I have given the impression that customers walk in with a checklist, they do not. They come with an expectation that your business will be clean and run in a hygienic way and what they do will be to form a series of impressions, very quickly, as they move through the service encounter. Then if they spot things that are wrong they will look for other things to support and build up that negative picture. Clearly though, the message is, do all you can to keep that impression positive.

An issue that also affects to a certain extent much of the contents of this book is the training of staff. Since the Food Safety (General Food Hygiene) Regulations 1995 and the requirement for food handlers engaged in the food business to be supervised and instructed and/or trained in food hygiene matters in line with the job that they do, there has been a large increase in food hygiene training activity.

But has all the increased training had an effect on the standards of food hygiene in any catering or food retail setting? There has been a lot of debate on this subject and the jury is probably still out. It is a generally held view that a certificate for food hygiene training is no guarantee that

the knowledge will be put into practice. Taylor (1996) claimed that training courses in food hygiene increase knowledge, but that any improvements are short lived. She recommended that food hygiene qualifications need to be more competency based to ensure that knowledge is translated into positive action.

In a similar vein Rennie (1995) claimed that there was a lack of evidence of improved food hygiene resulting from training programmes. Improvements in the standards of food hygiene would only happen, in her view, where there was good supervision and workplace reinforcement of messages and incentives to adopt new behaviour.

All the results of the research suggest a lack of progress from training to a change in practice – a so-called theory/practice divide. Knowing that the public are looking for the clues listed in this book may act as an incentive for some staff to put their knowledge into practice more frequently. A comment by one respondent to the research claimed that she looks for staff to do things in a similar way as evidence of training. She stated:

> In [name of restaurant withheld] they've got their training right because all the staff do things in the same way and you're not queuing up thinking, 'Oh, I hope I don't get her!' (Female: 35 – 44)

A prime example of a training need was demonstrated to me recently while visiting one of a popular chain of fast food restaurants. My wife and I were enjoying a nice cup of tea when our attention was drawn to the activities being carried out by an assistant who I shall, for the purposes of this account, call Dave. Dave was clearing and wiping off tables. During this task he noticed that the surround to the waste bin was in need of cleaning too, so he enthusiastically tackled this job. Then the state of an area of floor adjacent to the public entrance attracted his attention and this was duly wiped. After this was completed he returned to table cleaning – all with the same cloth! As these were being finished Dave was summoned to help serve a sudden influx of customers, which I noticed involved handling open food. Needless to say his hands were never washed. By all accounts the supervisor also failed to pick up on these problems. Multi-tasking is very common in the catering industry, but it must be accompanied by adequate training.

In essence though, effective training in whatever form it takes is important, not just in food hygiene but in all aspects of the business relevant to that member of staff's likely experiences. A management and supervisory regime that encourages good practice should then support that training. There now follows in the appendices a series of checklists so that you can audit a business for food hygiene and general cleanliness from a customer's perspective. This will give you an instant check on how a business is performing through the eyes of a typical customer. The checklists also permit you to write down improvements where you consider they need to be made.

Food hygiene is a legal requirement – and it needs to be, to protect public health, to protect consumers and to ensure that minimum standards exist. After all there will always be those who flout the law and who severely cut corners, and who by doing so will put people's health at risk. They deserve everything that the law can throw at them. However, the vast majority in the industry are law abiding and for them I believe food hygiene should increasingly be viewed as part of providing their customers with a quality service. In this way we can move away from the mindset commonly adopted by many that food hygiene and cleanliness are legal requirements only and nothing to do with attracting and keeping customers.

The research outlined in this book demonstrates that high standards of food hygiene and general cleanliness are important to customers and they take those high standards for granted. By anticipating and delivering those high standards you will continue to satisfy customers' demands in this aspect of the business and should succeed over competitors who do not.

Appendix:
Checklists

The checklists which follow contain the clues which both members of the public and the professionals involved in the research project, on which this book is founded, claimed to be either 'very important' or 'important' when assessing the standards of food hygiene and cleanliness in any catering establishment.

The checklists will guide you through your business in a logical manner and will help you and your staff to check that everything is in order and that the business is presenting the best face possible to attract and maintain customer involvement, as far as food hygiene and cleanliness are concerned.

Each checklist is divided into columns, one for the clue (factor), a yes/no column to provide an instant compliance check and then a column each for comments and any action necessary. In addition there is some space for you to write notes.

It is important to remember that the points listed in these checklists are nothing to do with compliance with food safety and hygiene laws. If you are concerned about these issues then you should contact your local authority environmental health department, consultant or legal adviser for advice.

Checklist 1

Theme: **Outside the business**
Business ....
Location: ....
Auditor: ....
Date: .... Time: ....

Factor	Yes	No	Comments	Action
The rubbish areas are clean and tidy.				
The rubbish bins are not overflowing.				
There are no untidy accumulations of rubbish outside the business.				
The outside of the premises is clean.				
The approach and entrance to the premises are clean.				

Notes:
....
....
....
....
....
....
....

....
....
....
....
....
....
....
....
....
....
....
....
....
....
....
....
....
....
....
....
....
....
....
....
....
....
....
....
....
....
....
....
....
....
....
....
....

Checklist 2

Theme: **Inside the business**

Business: ....

Location: ....

Auditor: ....

Date: .... Time: ....

Factor	Yes	No	Comments	Action
There is a general impression of cleanliness as customers walk into the business.				
The reception area is clean.				
There are no unpleasant smells in the premises, such as stale cooking smells.				
The premises are in good decorative order.				
The premises are tidy throughout with no undue clutter.				
All the floors including the carpets are clean.				

Factor	Yes	No	Comments	Action
All the walls are clean.				
All the ceilings are clean.				
All the windows are clean.				
All the curtains and blinds are clean.				
All the bar areas are clean and free from dust.				
Equipment is clean.				
Training certificates on display in the premises are relatively up to date and relate to current employees.				
There are no flies in the premises, especially near any food service areas.				
There is no evidence of any rodent infestations in the premises.				

Factor	Yes	No	Comments	Action
There are no pet animals in the premises.				
Rubbish and food waste are placed in lidded bins.				
Rubbish is not permitted to accumulate in food preparation and service areas.				
All parts of the kitchen (if visible) including any equipment is clean and tidy.				
All the food service areas and surfaces are clean.				
There are measures taken to prevent contamination by customers at salad bars and open food displays.				
Wiping cloths used are clean.				

Factor	Yes	No	Comments	Action
Cloths used for the serving of food are clean.				
Dishes used for the serving or presentation of food are clean.				
Spoons, forks, slices, etc. used for the serving of food are clean.				
Where raw and cooked foods are on display, there are separate utensils/ equipment used for each.				
The toilets are clean, including pans, urinals, and wash hand basins.				
There is a good supply of toilet paper.				
There is hot and cold water at the wash hand basins.				

Factor	Yes	No	Comments	Action
There is a good supply of soap at the wash hand basins.				
There are hand drying facilities available at the wash hand basins (paper towels or hot air hand driers are preferred).				
Where there are signs in the toilets stating that they are cleaned regularly, they have been 'signed off'.				

Notes:

....

....

....

....

....

....

....

....

....

....

....

....

....

Checklist 3

Theme: **Staff working in the business**

Business: ....

Location: ....

Auditor: ....

Date: .... Time: ....

Factor	Yes	No	Comments	Action
The staff are polite, friendly and courteous.				
The staff look clean and smart.				
The staff are wearing obvious work clothing or uniforms.				
All clothing worn for work is clean.				
Staff who are cooking or preparing food are wearing clean overalls.				
Aprons being worn are clean.				

Factor	Yes	No	Comments	Action
The staff's hair is clean, tidy and, if long, tied back.				
Staff who are cooking or preparing food are wearing hats.				
The staff's hands and fingernails are clean.				
The staff are not wearing any nail-varnish.				
Any cuts or grazes on staff's hands are covered with a coloured waterproof dressing.				
Staff are seen to wash their hands on occasions.				
The staff are wearing a minimum of jewellery.				
The staff are not wearing any strong smelling perfume or aftershave.				

Factor	Yes	No	Comments	Action
If staff cough or sneeze is it away from uncovered food.				
Staff that are seen to blow their nose are also seen to wash their hands.				
Staff are never seen dipping their fingers into food and licking them to taste.				
Staff are seen to avoid any poor personal habits, such as fiddling with their hair, touching their nose, etc.				
Staff are never seen smoking on duty				
Staff are not seen eating on duty				
Staff handle cutlery, glassware, etc. correctly, ie never by the rim or part coming into contact with the customer's mouth.				

Factor	Yes	No	Comments	Action
Staff do not touch the food when they serve it.				
Staff use tongs, slices or spoons for serving food.				
Staff that cook, prepare or serve food are never seen to handle money.				
Food is served with care and attention.				
There is good separation of job roles of staff, eg they are not sweeping floors one minute and serving food the next.				
Staff who clear and clean tables have a positive and attentive attitude.				

Notes:

....
....
....
....
....
....
....
....
....
....
....
....
....
....
....
....
....
....
....
....
....
....
....
....
....
....
....
....
....
....
....
....
....
....
....
....
....
....
....
....
....

Checklist 4

Theme: **The table and immediate environment**

Business: ....

Location: ....

Auditor: ....

Date: .... Time: ....

Factor	Yes	No	Comments	Action
The areas around and under the tables are clean and free from waste.				
The seats, stools and benches are clean.				
High chairs and booster seats are clean.				
Trays are clean and dry.				
The tables are clean.				
Cloths used to clean the tables are clean.				
The tables are cleared and cleaned quickly between customers.				

Factor	Yes	No	Comments	Action
The tablecloths are clean.				
The tablemats are clean.				
The napkins are clean.				
The menus are clean and not stained.				
The cutlery is clean and free from watermarks.				
The crockery is clean and free from watermarks.				
The crockery is free from chips and cracks.				
The glassware is clean and free from watermarks.				
The teapots/coffeepots are clean.				
The salt and pepper containers are clean.				

Factor	Yes	No	Comments	Action
The sauce accompaniment containers are clean and free from build-up.				
The ashtrays are cleaned and emptied regularly.				

Notes:

....
....
....
....
....
....
....
....
....
....
....
....
....
....
....
....
....
....
....
....
....

Checklist 5

Theme: **The food and drink**

Business: ....

Location: ....

Auditor: ....

Date: .... Time: ....

Factor	Yes	No	Comments	Action
The food on display is protected from contamination.				
The food on display looks fresh.				
The food on display is well presented.				
The salad stuffs are well washed.				
Cold meats, cooked fish, egg products, salad stuffs, sweet and cream foods are on chilled display.				
The hot foods on display are piping hot.				

Factor	Yes	No	Comments	Action
All dishes of hot and cold food on display are changed when the dish is empty and not topped up.				
All packet and wrapped foods are within their 'use-by' or 'best-before' dates.				
Fresh fruit on display is not over-ripe.				
All cold foods are served cold.				
All hot foods are served hot.				
The food is cooked properly right the way through, unless ordered otherwise.				
The hot food does not appear to have been warmed up.				
The food served is free from excess fat or grease.				

Factor	Yes	No	Comments	Action
The hot food is served on hot plates.				
The food is well presented on the plate.				
Condiments, including sauces, relishes, pickles and other accompaniments, are fresh.				
Cold drinks are served cold.				
Fizzy drinks are fizzy.				
There are no complaints received about physical contamination of the food.				

Notes:

....

....

....

....

....

....

....

References

Audit Commission (1991) *Towards a Healthier Environment: Managing Environmental Health Services*. London: HMSO.

Auty, S. (1992) 'Consumer choice and segmentation in the restaurant industry', *Service Industry Journal*, vol. 12, No. 3, pp 324 – 9.

Booker, C. and North, R. (1994) The Mad Officials. London: Constable.

British Broadcasting Corporation (1979) *Fawlty Towers – Basil the Rat*. London: British Broadcasting Corporation.

Department of Trade and Industry (1999) *Modern Markets: Confident Consumers*, Cm 4410. London: Stationery Office.

Drucker, P. F. (1989) *The Practice of Management*. Oxford: Heinemann Professional.

East, J. P. (1993) *Managing Quality in the Catering Industry*. Kingston-upon-Thames, Surrey: Croner Publications.

Engel, J. F. Blackwell, R. D. and Miniard, P. W. (1986) *Consumer Behaviour*, 5th edn. Tokyo: Dryden Process.

Festinger, L. (1957) *A Theory of Cognitive Dissonance*. Stanford, CA: Stanford University Press.

Finkelstein, J. (1989) *Dining Out: A Sociology of Modern Manners*. Cambridge: Polity Press.

Food Safety Act 1990. London: HMSO.

Food Safety (General Food Hygiene) Regulations 1995, SI No. 1763. London: HMSO.

Food Standards Act 1999. London: Stationery Office.

Food Standards Agency (2000) Food Safety Act 1990. *Code of Practice No. 9:*

Food Hygiene Inspections (Second Revision October 2000) London: Food Standards Agency.

Food Standards Agency (2001a) *Framework Agreement on Local Authority Food Law Enforcement.* London: Food Standards Agency.

Food Standards Agency (2001b). Strategic Plan 2001 – 2006 – *Putting Consumers First.* London: Food Standards Agency.

Food Standards Agency (2002a). *Consumer Attitudes to Food Standards.* London: Food Standards Agency.

Food Standards Agency (2002b) *Report on Local Authority Food Law Enforcement Activity in the UK.* London: Food Standards Agency.

Goode, J. Beardsworth, A. Haslam, C., Keil T. and Sherratt, E. (1995) 'Dietary dilemmas. nutritional concerns of the 1990s', *British Food Journal,* vol.97, no 11, pp. 3 – 12.

Guerrier, Y., Kipps, M., Lockwood, A. and Sheppard, J. (1992) 'Perceptions of hygiene and quality in the food service operation', in Cooper, C. P. and Lockwood, A. (eds), *Progress in Tourism, Recreation and Hospitality Management,* Vol. 4. London: Bellhaven Press, pp. 182 – 94.

Johns, N. and Howard, A. (1998) 'Customer expectations versus perceptions of service performance in the food service industry'. *International Journal of Service Industry Management,* vol. 9, No. 3, pp. 248 – 265.

Lancaster, G. and Massingham, L. (1993) Essentials of Marketing, 2nd edn. Maidenhead McGraw-Hill.

Leach, J. C. (1999) *Food Hygiene in Public Eating Places – A Comparative Study of Public and Professional Perceptions in the Wealden District of East Sussex.* PhD thesis, University of Brighton.

Leighton, C. and Bent, R. (1997) 'Complaints handling and staff training by UK food retailers', *British Food Journal,* Vol. 99, No. 5, pp. 159 – 67.

Lewis, R. C. (1981) 'Restaurant advertising: appeals and consumer intentions', *Journal of Advertising Research*, Vol. 21, no. 5. pp. 69 – 74.

Local Authorities Coordinating Body on Food and Trading Standards (1994) *Enforcement Myths*. Croydon: Local Authorities Coordinating Body on Food and Trading Standards.

McMahon, P. S. and Schmelzer, C. D. (1989) 'The role of the customer in the food service encounter', *Hospitality Education and Research Journal*. Vol. 13, No. 3, pp. 427 – 34.

Ministry of Agriculture, Fisheries and Food. (1991 – 97). *Summary of Official Returns 1991 – 1997*. London: Ministry of Agriculture, Fisheries and Food.

Ministry of Agriculture, Fisheries and Food, Department of Health, Scottish Office and Welsh Offices. (1991) *Food Safety Act 1990. Code of Practice No 3: Inspection Procedures – General*. London: HMSO.

Ministry of Agriculture, Fisheries and Food (1998) *The Food Standards Agency – A Force for Change*, Cm 3830. London: Stationery Office.

New Labour (1997) New Labour – *Because Britain Deserves Better*. London: Labour Party.

Reber, A. S. (1985) *The Penguin Dictionary of Psychology*. Harmondsworth Penguin Books.

Rennie, D. M. (1995) 'Health education models and food hygiene education', *Journal of the Royal Society of Health*, Vol. 115, No. 5, pp. 75 – 9.

Roberts, D. (1982) 'Factors contributing to outbreaks of food poisoning in England and Wales 1970 – 1979', *Journal of Hygiene*, Vol. 89, pp. 491 – 8.

Taylor, E. (1996) 'Is food hygiene training really effective?', *Environmental Health*, vol: 104, no. 9, pp. 275 – 6.

Wheelock, V. J. (1992) 'Food quality and consumer choice', *British Food Journal.* Vol. 94, no. 3, pp. 39 – 43.

Zeithaml, V. A., Parasuraman, A. and Berry, L. (1990) *Delivering Quality Service – Balancing Customer Perceptions and Expectations,* New York: Free Press.